TOTALLY DOTTY DOT-TO-DOTS

This edition published by Parragon Books Ltd in 2017

Parragon Books Ltd
Chartist House
15–17 Trim Street
Bath BA1 1HA, UK
www.parragon.com

Written by Susan Fairbrother
Illustrated by Beatrice Costamagna, Dean Gray and Matthew Scott

ISBN 978-1-4748-2028-8

Printed in China

TOTALLY DOTTY DOT-TO-DOTS

PaRragon

Bath • New York • Cologne • Melbourne • Delhi
Hong Kong • Shenzhen • Singapore

What's going on
at the farm?

4

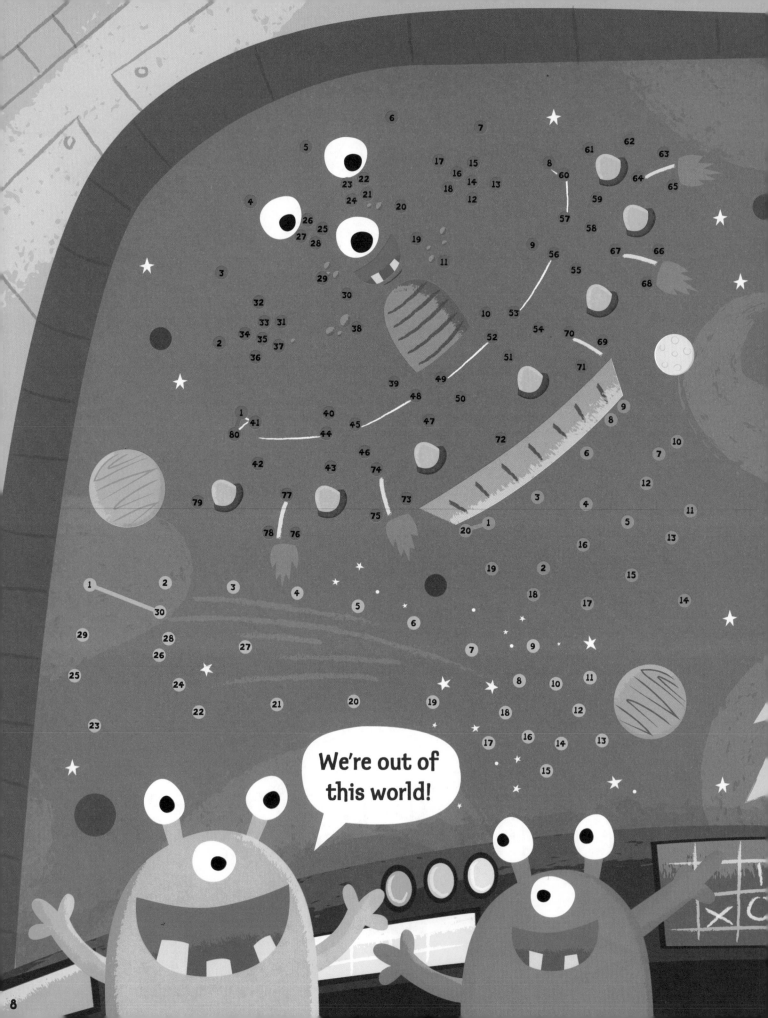

Make a wish...

Crack!

Crack!

Crack!

Crack!

Hello, world!

13

14

The garden's full of
creepy-crawlies.

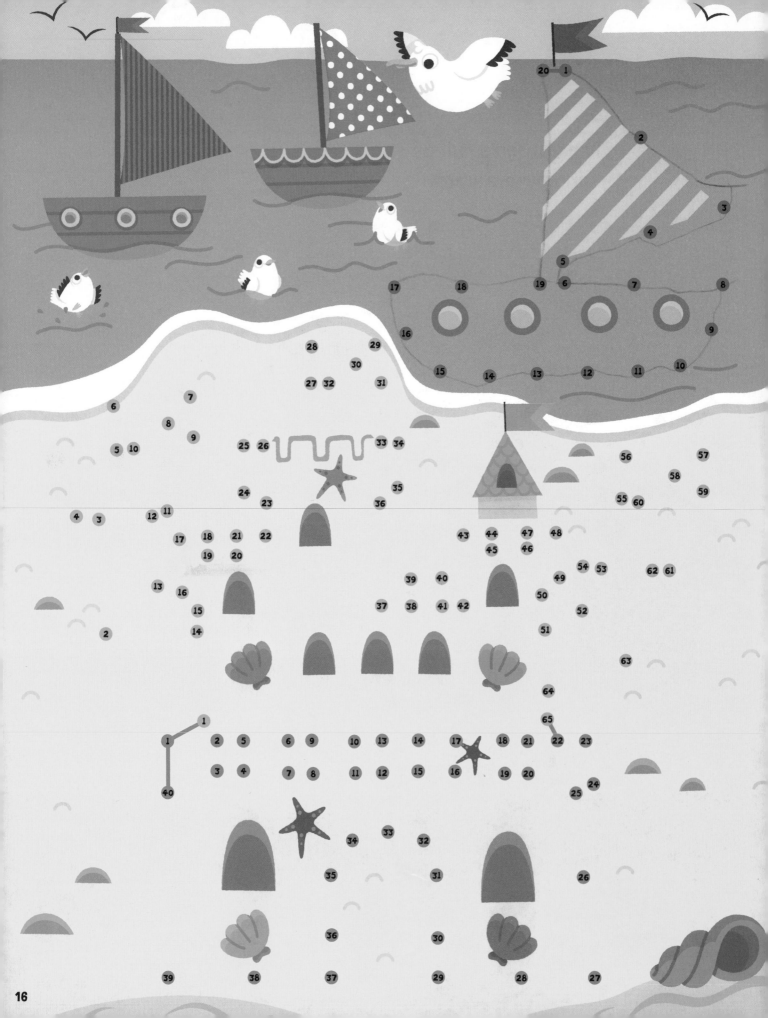

What can you see beside the sea?

That's not Grandma...

22

Everybody freeze!

We're coming to the rescue!

26

Spot the dot-to-dot odd one out.

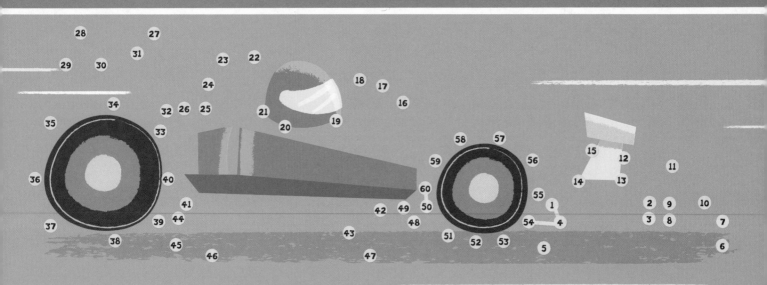

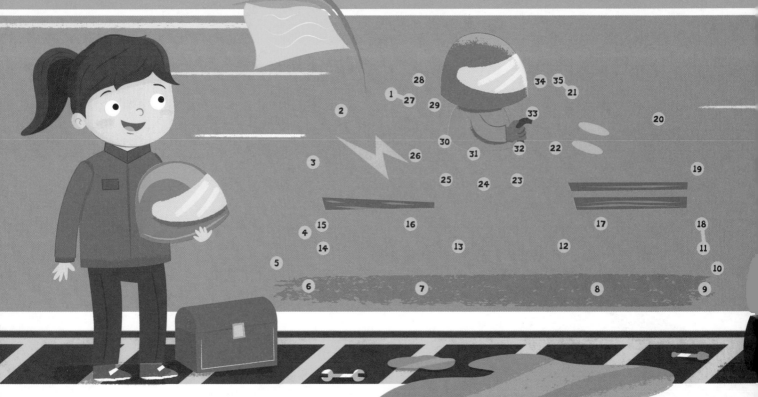

Take a trip under the ocean.

They're friendly!

It's the great Stupendo!
He can read minds...

40

Boing!

Boing!

Everyone's on the move.

49

Once upon a time, in a tumbledown castle, there lived...

Roar!

52

Let's finish the other half.

Hissss!

There's plenty
to share!

58

There's fairy dust everywhere.

Zooooom!

What a mess!

I think they've made friends.

71

I don't know what you are...

72

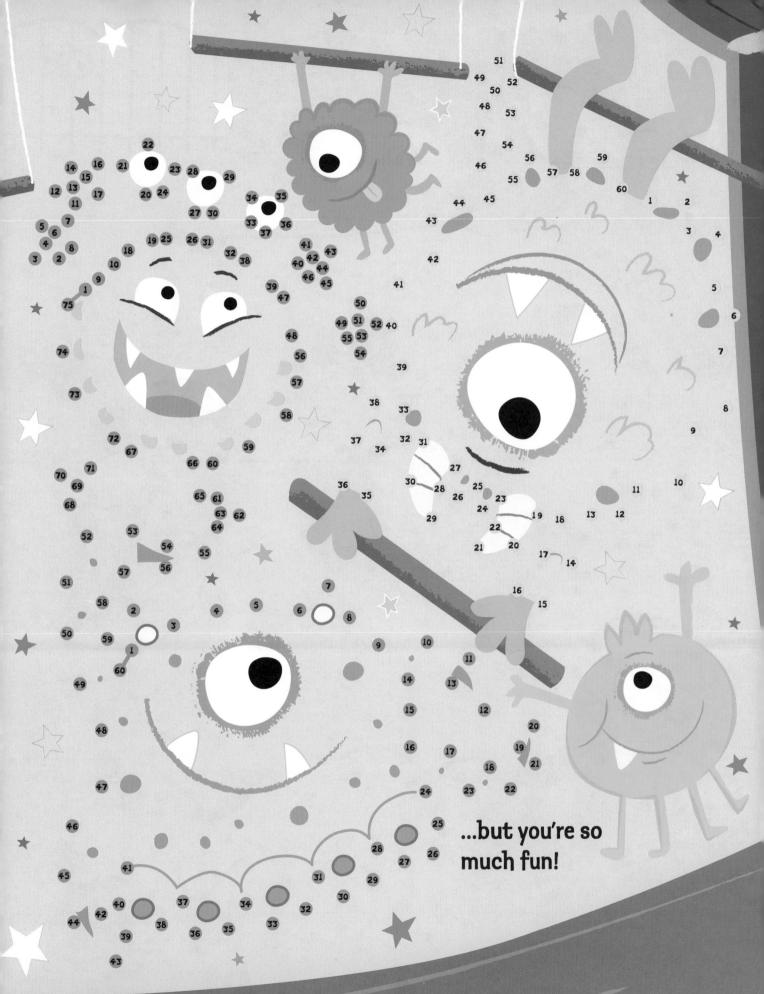

...but you're so much fun!

73

Who do you think lives here?

80

Eek!

83

Make my garden grow.

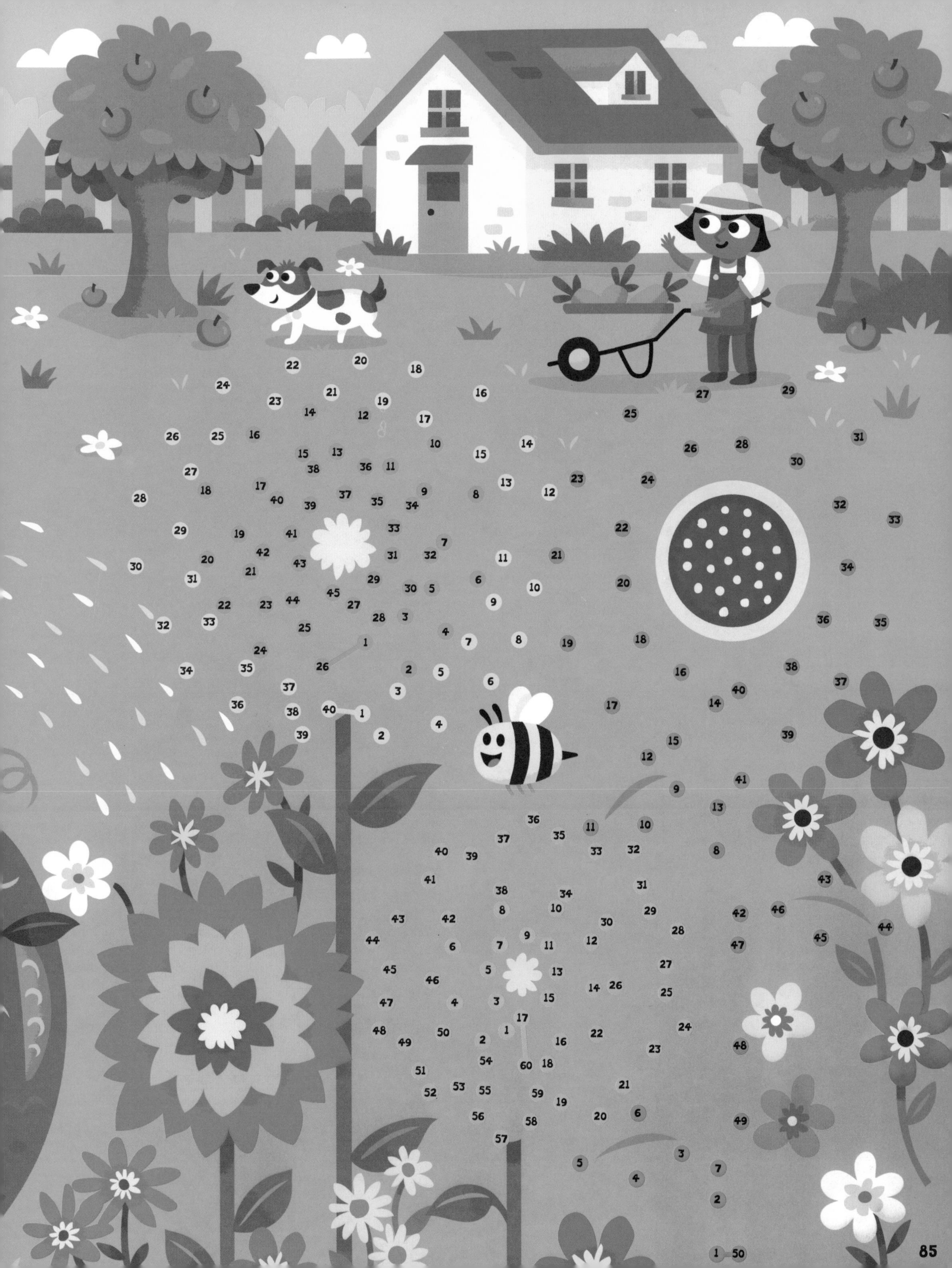

Take a twirl.

Where are we?

We love playing
in the snow!

A new hairdo for you?

There's lots to
see on this tour.

Mirror, mirror, on the wall...

...who's the fairest of them all?

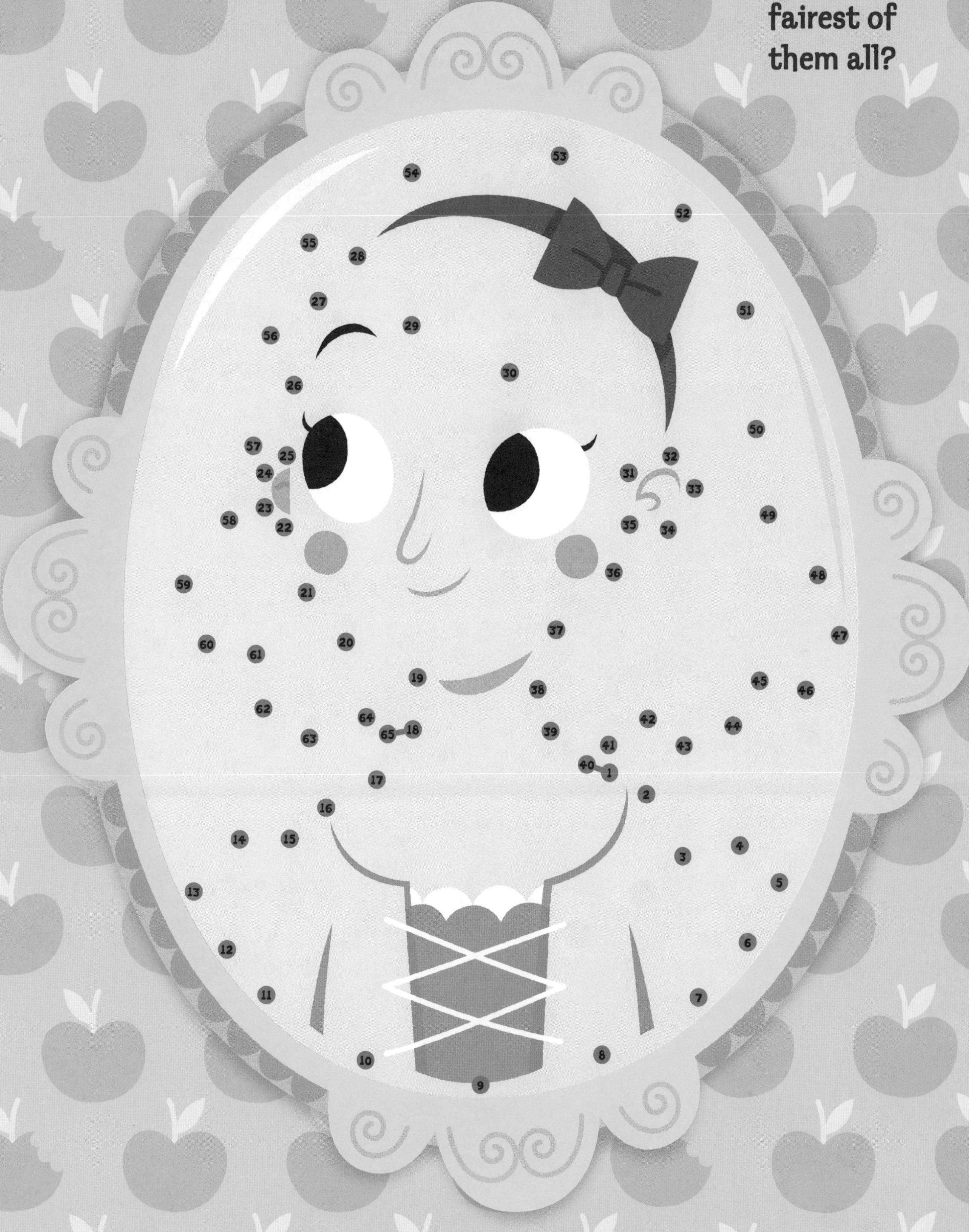

Watch your step!

100

Spot which dot-to-dot animals are lost.

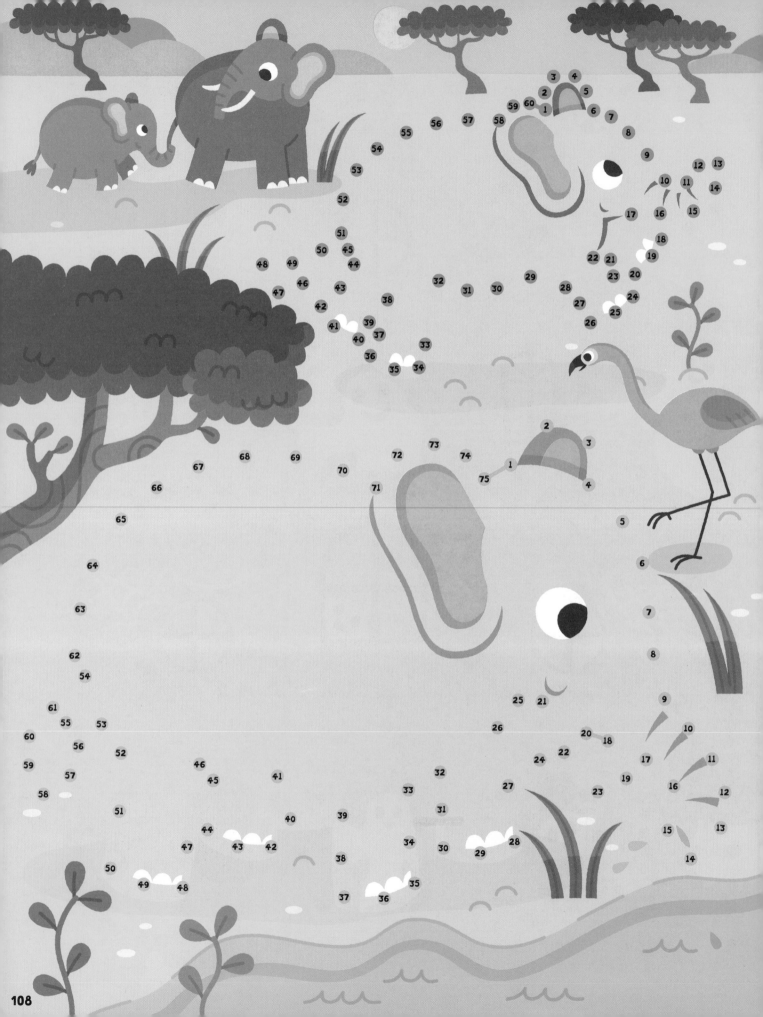

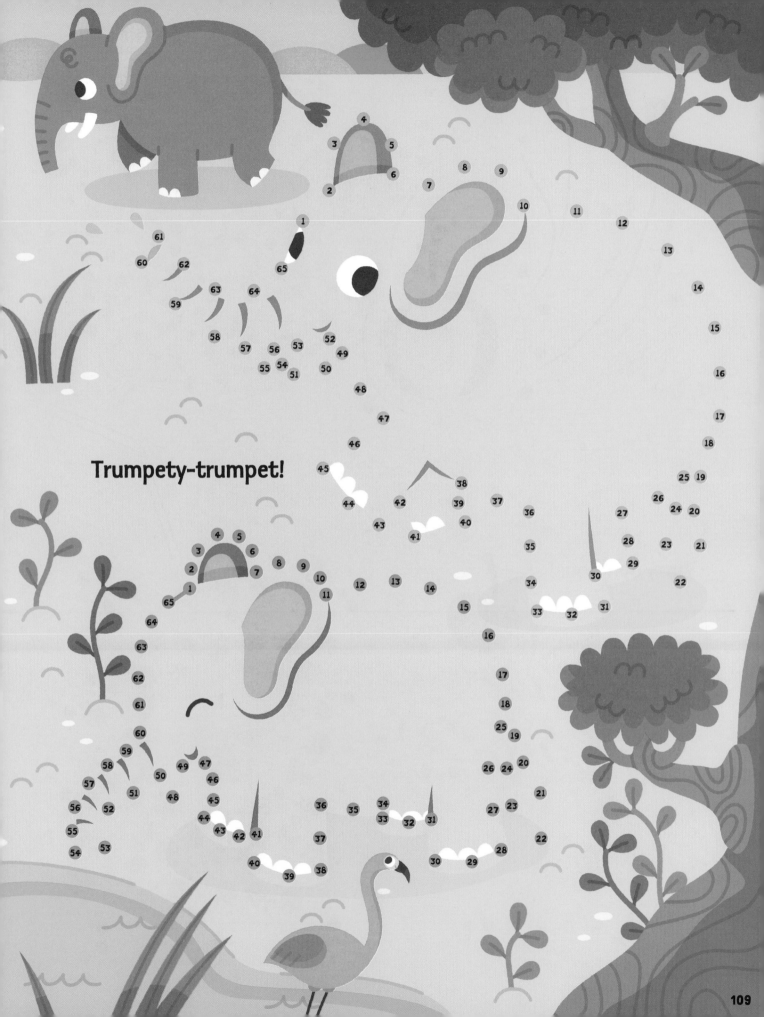

Trumpety-trumpet!

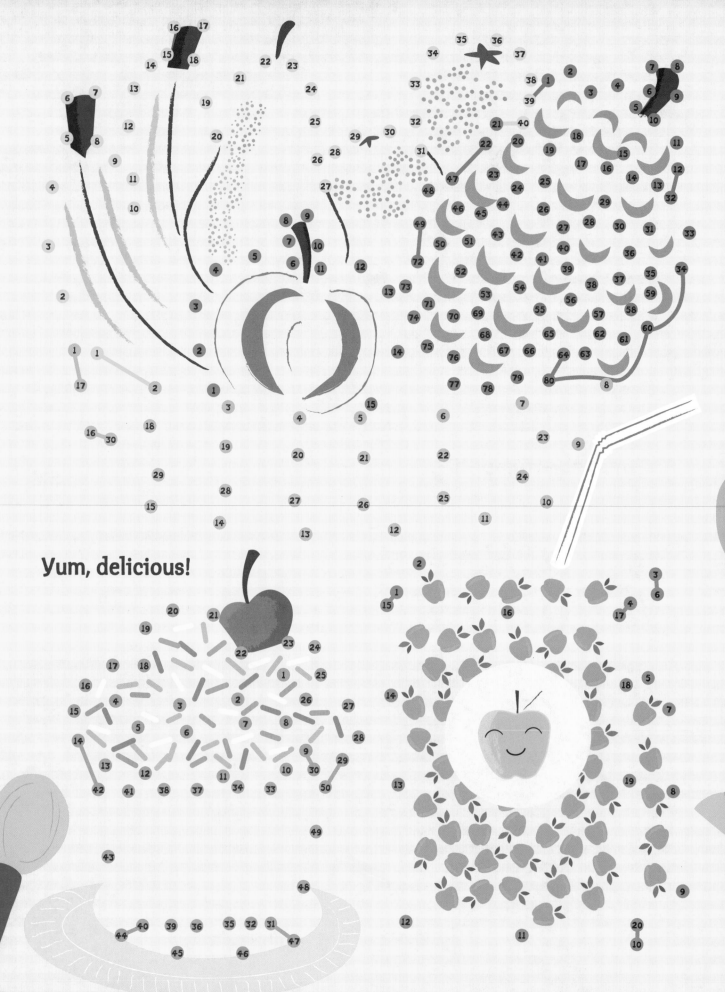

Yum, delicious!

Welcome to the big city.

Be a fashion designer! Dot-to-dot some super-stylish outfits.

This is awesome!

Flap

Flap

Flap

122

Tweet

Tweet

Solutions

Pages 4-5

Pages 6-7

Pages 8-9
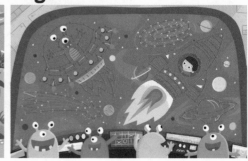

Pages 10-11

Pages 12-13

Pages 14-15

Pages 16-17

Pages 18-19

Pages 20-21

Pages 22-23

Pages 24-25

Pages 26-27

Pages 28-29

Pages 30-31

Pages 32-33

Pages 34-35
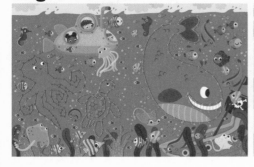

Pages 36-37

Pages 38-39

Pages 40-41

Pages 42-43

Pages 44-45

Pages 46-47

Pages 48-49

Pages 50-51

Pages 52-53

Pages 54-55

Pages 56-57

Pages 58-59

Pages 60-61

Pages 62-63

Pages 64-65

Pages 66-67

Pages 68-69

Pages 70-71

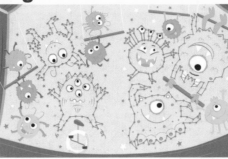

Pages 72-73

Pages 74-75

Pages 76-77

Pages 78-79

Pages 80-81

Pages 82-83

Pages 84-85

Pages 86-87

Pages 88-89

Pages 90-91

Pages 92-93

Pages 94-95

Pages 96-97

Pages 98-99

Pages 100-101

Pages 102-103

Pages 104-105

Pages 106-107

Pages 108-109

Pages 110-111

Pages 112-113

Pages 114-115

Pages 116-117

Pages 118-119

Pages 120-121
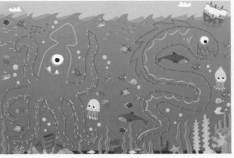

Pages 122-123